11+ NUMERICAL REASONING

Multi-Part Numerical Reasoning

Book 1

Short Tests 1 –10

How to use this pack to make the most of 11+ exam preparation

It is important to remember that for 11 plus exams there is no national syllabus, no pass mark and no retake option! It is therefore vitally important that your child is fully primed in order to perform to the best of their ability to give themselves the best possible chance on the day.

Unlike similar publications, the First Past the Post® series uniquely assesses your child's performance on a question-by-question basis, helping to identify areas for improvement and providing suggestions for further targeted tests.

Numerical Reasoning

This series of mini-tests is representative of the numerical reasoning section of contemporary multi-discipline 11+ tests, which typically have two papers. One paper usually has a long worded numerical reasoning problems section and the other contains short, quick fire questions more akin to traditional maths. This publication addresses the former. The suggested time is provided based on classroom testing sessions held at our centre.

Never has it been more useful to learn from mistakes!

Students can improve by as much as 15 percent not only by focused practice but also by targeting any weak areas.

How to manage your child's own practice

To get the most up-to-date information log on to the ElevenPlusExams website (www.elevenplusexams.co.uk). ElevenPlusExams is the largest UK on-line resource with over 40,000 webpages and a forum administered by a select group of experienced moderators.

About the authors

The ElevenPlusExams **First Past the Post®** series has been created by a team of experienced tutors and authors from leading British universities including Oxford and Cambridge.

Published by University of Buckingham Press

With special thanks to the children who tested our material at the ElevenPlusExams centre in Harrow.

ISBN: 9781908684301

Copyright © ElevenPlusExams.co.uk 2013

Contents Page

This workbook is comprised of ten Short Tests, made up of five multi-part questions and each should take 15 minutes to complete.

Once you have completed each test, using the answers and explanations; mark the Short Tests and upload them onto our 11+ Peer Compare System™ to see how well you performed in comparison to others who have taken this test.

You can register by visiting www.ElevenPlusExams.co.uk/FirstPastThePost to post your results anonymously and obtain the feedback.

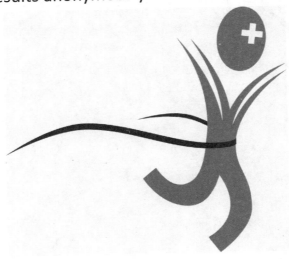

Instructions

In this book there are boxes given to you in which to write your answers, such as the one below:

Place value is determined by which box you choose to write your numbers in, for example the correct way to write '10' is shown below:

If the answer is a negative value, use one of the answer boxes to write a negative sign as shown below:

Some questions are multiple choice, when this is the case there will be a box underneath each answer for you to mark your answer in. The correct way to do so is with a line through the box, as shown below; **do not** circle it.

Numerical Reasoning
Short Test 1

	Marking Grid																										Total:
Question	**1**					**2**					**3**					**4**					**5**					
	a	b	c	d	e	a	b	c	d	e	a	b	c	d	e	a	b	c	d	e	a	b	c	d	e	
✓ Or ✗										▓					▓										▓	/22

Read the following instructions carefully:

1. You have 15 minutes to complete this test of 5 multi-part questions.

2. Work as quickly and carefully as you can.

3. When you have finished a page, go straight onto the next page until you finish the test.

4. You can use all the available space around the question to do your working, however only write the answer in the answer boxes.

5. To change an answer, either rub out your original answer or put a single line through it and note down the new answer, aligning it to any answer boxes.

6. If you cannot answer a question, go on to the next question.

7. When you have completed this paper go back to any questions you have missed out and check your answers.

8. Calculators and protractors are not permitted in this test.

Good luck!

After you have finished this paper you can use the <u>11+ Peer Compare System</u>[TM] to see how well you performed compared to others who have taken this test. You can register by visiting <u>www.ElevenPlusExams.co.uk/FirstPastThePost</u> to post your results anonymously and obtain the feedback.

Question 1

Jack and Dean chose a DVD movie to watch.

a. The movie lasts for 2 hours and 20 minutes. What is this expressed as a mixed fraction?

$$\boxed{}\ \frac{\boxed{}}{\boxed{}}\ \textbf{hour(s)}$$

b. The DVD had 1 hour and 50 minutes of special features. What is this expressed as a mixed fraction?

$$\boxed{}\ \frac{\boxed{}}{\boxed{}}\ \textbf{hour(s)}$$

c. What is the total running time of the movie and special features on the DVD?

$$\boxed{}\ \boxed{}\ \boxed{}\ \textbf{minute(s)}$$

d. What percentage of the DVD's total running time is special features?

$$\boxed{}\ \boxed{}\ \boxed{}\ \textbf{\%}$$

e. What is the total running time of the whole DVD in hours, expressed as a mixed fraction?

$$\boxed{}\ \frac{\boxed{}}{\boxed{}}\ \textbf{hour(s)}$$

Question 2

The following questions refer to the numbers below.

A	3.45
B	8.14109
C	4.50521
D	2.49479
E	6.85891

a. Mark the number's letter that is closest to 7 units, 9 tenths and 6 hundredths?

A ⬭   B ⬭   C ⬭   D ⬭   E ⬭

b. What is the value of (E + B) x A?

c. What is the value of (C + D)²?

d. Which number is the closest to 4?

A ⬭   B ⬭   C ⬭   D ⬭   E ⬭

Question 3

Ben is making a formula to calculate his grandfather's age. He is told his grandfather is 4 years less than 8 times his age.

Grandfather's age = f Ben's age = b

a. Mark the equation that Ben should use to calculate his grandfather's age.

$f = 6b - 4$ $f = 8b - 4$ $f = 7b - 4$ $f = 20b - 4$

b. Using the equation above if Ben is 8 years old, how old is his grandfather?

☐☐ **years**

c. In 2 years time Ben will be 10. How old will his grandfather be?

☐☐ **years**

The formula to calculate Ben's grandmother's age (m) is $m = 5b + 3$.

d. When Ben's grandmother is 63 years old, how old will Ben be?

☐☐ **years**

Question 4

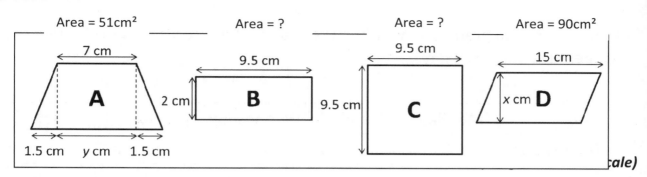

a. What is the length of *y* in shape A?

□□ . □□ cm

b. What is the perimeter of shape B?

□□ . □□ cm

c. Which shape has the largest area?

A ⬭   B ⬭   C ⬭   D ⬭

d. Which two shapes have approximately the same area? (Write the corresponding letters below)

□ and □

e. What is the value of *x* in shape D?

□□ . □□ cm

Question 5

Alison has started preparation for her 11+ exams. She records how much time she has spent revising each day.

Day	Monday	Tuesday	Wednesday	Thursday	Friday
Time Spent	1 hr 20 min	2 hr 30 min	45 min	1 hr 40 min	2 hr 15 min

a. What was the longest time that Alison spent revising in one day?

☐☐☐ **minute(s)**

b. What is the range of time that Alison spent revising?

☐ **hour(s)** ☐☐ **minute(s)**

c. What is the median amount of time that Alison spent revising?

☐ **hour(s)** ☐☐ **minute(s)**

d. What is the mean amount of time that Alison spent revising?

☐ **hour(s)** ☐☐ **minute(s)**

FIRST PAST THE POST® SERIES

Numerical Reasoning
Short Test 2

Question	Marking Grid																									Total:
	1					**2**					**3**					**4**					**5**					
	a	b	c	d	e	a	b	c	d	e	a	b	c	d	e	a	b	c	d	e	a	b	c	d	e	
✓ Or ✗					■					■					■					■					■	/20

Read the following instructions carefully:

1. You have 15 minutes to complete this test of 5 multi-part questions.

2. Work as quickly and carefully as you can.

3. When you have finished a page, go straight onto the next page until you finish the test.

4. You can use all the available space around the question to do your working, however only write the answer in the answer boxes.

5. To change an answer, either rub out your original answer or put a single line through it and note down the new answer, aligning it to any answer boxes.

6. If you cannot answer a question, go on to the next question.

7. When you have completed this paper go back to any questions you have missed out and check your answers.

8. Calculators and protractors are not permitted in this test.

Good luck!

Question 1

Ajay has 12 boxes each containing x blue pencils and 6 boxes each containing y red pencils.

a. Mark the equation representing the total number of pencils Ajay has.

$12x + 6$ ⬭ $6y + 12$ ⬭ $12x + 6y$ ⬭ $15x + 6y$ ⬭

b. Subsequently, if 7 boxes of x pencils are taken away, mark the new equation for the number of pencils Ajay would have.

$5x + 6y$ ⬭ $6y + 5$ ⬭ $12x + 6y$ ⬭ $17x + 6y$ ⬭

c. Thereafter, if $^1/_2$ the boxes containing y pencils are removed, mark the new equation showing the number of pencils Ajay would be left with.

$5x + 3y$ ⬭ $6y + 2$ ⬭ $6x + 6y$ ⬭ $10x + 3y$ ⬭

d. If $x = 3$ and $y = 5$, what is the value of the expression below?

$$2x + 5y + 4xy$$

Question 2

Demi is shopping for her 7 day holiday to Spain. She has saved £120 for the items she needs to buy before leaving for her holiday.

a. Prior to her trip, she purchases a sun hat and a digital camera for a total of £112.80. How much money does she have left?

b. If she spends half the remaining money from part (a) on fashion accessories, how much money does she now have remaining?

c. Demi has a total of £525 to spend whilst in Spain. On average, how much money can she spend each day?

d. If Demi spent 20% more than the average calculated in part (c) for 3 days, how much has she overspent by?

Question 3

James is conducting an experiment and has partially filled the beaker shown below with water.

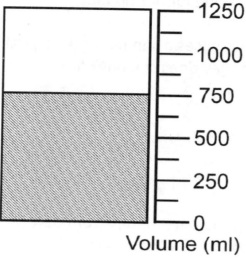

Volume (ml)

a. How much water is there in the beaker?

 ml

b. If James pours $\frac{1}{2}$ of the water out of the beaker, what volume of water is left in the beaker?

 ml

c. What is the capacity of this measuring beaker when full?

 l

d. For another experiment, James needs 25% more water than what he initially started with. What is the total volume of water required for his new experiment?

 ml

Question 4

Jack is paving his garden patio with paving stones. The patio measures 3.3m x 2.1m and each paving stone measures 30cm x 30cm.

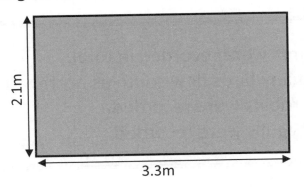 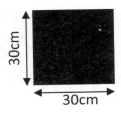

(Diagrams not to scale)

a. How many paving stones will fit along the 2.1m edge?

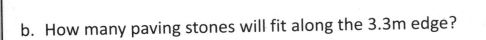

b. How many paving stones will fit along the 3.3m edge?

c. What is the area of her garden patio?

 m²

d. How many paving stones will Jack need to pave the whole patio?

Question 5

A group of year 5 children conducted a study on the types of birds they saw fly over the field outside their school. Their results are shown below.

> 186 birds were recorded in total.
> Twice as many birds flew south as north.
> 6 robins were recorded.
> 15 gulls were recorded.

a. If the only birds that were recorded were robins, gulls and pigeons, how many pigeons flew over the field?

b. How many birds flew south?

c. If this study lasted three hours, what was the average number of birds recorded each hour of the study?

d. What is the ratio of gulls to robins seen in this study?

Numerical Reasoning
Short Test 3

Question																										Total:
	1					**2**					**3**					**4**					**5**					
	a	b	c	d	e	a	b	c	d	e	a	b	c	d	e	a	b	c	d	e	a	b	c	d	e	
✓ Or ✗					■																					/24

Marking Grid

Read the following instructions carefully:

1. You have 15 minutes to complete this test of 5 multi-part questions.

2. Work as quickly and carefully as you can.

3. When you have finished a page, go straight onto the next page until you finish the test.

4. You can use all the available space around the question to do your working, however only write the answer in the answer boxes.

5. To change an answer, either rub out your original answer or put a single line through it and note down the new answer, aligning it to any answer boxes.

6. If you cannot answer a question, go on to the next question.

7. When you have completed this paper go back to any questions you have missed out and check your answers.

8. Calculators and protractors are not permitted in this test.

Good luck!

After you have finished this paper you can use the <u>11+ Peer Compare System</u>™ to see how well you performed compared to others who have taken this test. You can register by visiting <u>www.ElevenPlusExams.co.uk/FirstPastThePost</u> to post your results anonymously and obtain the feedback.

Question 1

Ricky lives on Sudbury Lane and takes the bus regularly. Below is the timetable of the bus route he uses.

Stop	Monday to Friday	Saturday
Sudbury Lane	10:00	12:15
Wembley Park	10:09	12:30
Preston Road	10:31	12:47
Preston Hill	10:44	13:05

a. On a Monday, how long does the journey take from Sudbury Lane to Wembley Park?

[   ][   ][   ][   ] **seconds**

b. Mark the journey that takes the least time on a Thursday.

Preston Road to Preston Hill ⬭

Wembley Park to Preston Road ⬭

c. Mark the day on which travelling from Preston Road to Preston Hill is shorter.

Saturday ⬭

Thursday ⬭

d. If on a particular Saturday road works increase journey times by 20%, how long will it now take Ricky to travel from Sudbury Lane to Wembley Park?

[   ][   ][   ][   ] **seconds**

Question 2

In the sequence below, missing terms are represented by the letters A, B and C.

$$A, \quad 3, \quad 6, \quad 12, \quad 24, \quad 48, \quad B, \quad C$$

a. What is the value of term B?

b. What is the sum of the terms B and C?

c. What is the value of term A?

d. How many of the terms, excluding A, B and C, are multiples of 4?

e. How many of the terms above, excluding A, B and C, are triangular numbers?

Question 3

The pie chart below shows the favourite subjects of 200 children in year 6.

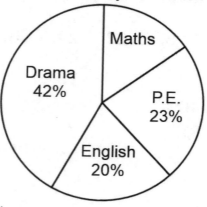

(Diagram not to scale)

a. What percentage said maths was their favourite subject?

b. How many students said English was their favourite subject?

c. If $^3/_8$ of the pupils who said English was their favourite subject are girls, how many girls does this represent?

d. Using your answer from part (c), how many boys said English was their favourite subject?

e. How many degrees does the segment for English represent?

Question 4

Adrian is saving money for a bike whilst donating to charity. Of his weekly £15 pocket money, Adrian donates $^1/_3$ to charity and the remaining $^2/_3$ is saved towards the bike.

a. How much money is put towards the bike every week?

£ ⬜⬜ . ⬜⬜

b. After 4 weeks how much money has Adrian donated to charity?

£ ⬜⬜ . ⬜⬜

c. After x weeks, Adrian has donated £55 to charity. What is the value of x?

⬜⬜

d. If the bike costs £120, what percentage towards the cost of the bike has he saved after 9 weeks?

⬜⬜⬜ %

e. If the bike is on sale and now costs £100, once Adrian has saved enough to purchase the bike, how much would he have donated to charity?

£ ⬜⬜ . ⬜⬜

Question 5

The Venn diagram below provides information about 40 children who own dogs, fish, or neither of the two.

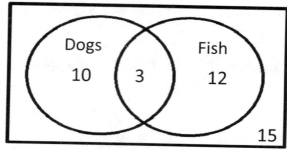

a. How many children own both dogs and fish?

b. How many children do not own either of the two pets?

c. As a fraction of the total number of children, how many children own fish?

d. What is the ratio of only dogs owned to only fish owned?

e. If 20% of children with neither of the two pets decided to get a dog, how many children would now own dogs?

Numerical Reasoning
Short Test 4

Question	Marking Grid																									Total:
	1					**2**					**3**					**4**					**5**					
	a	b	c	d	e	a	b	c	d	e	a	b	c	d	e	a	b	c	d	e	a	b	c	d	e	
✓ Or ✗				▓					▓																	/23

Read the following instructions carefully:

1. You have 15 minutes to complete this test of 5 multi-part questions.

2. Work as quickly and carefully as you can.

3. When you have finished a page, go straight onto the next page until you finish the test.

4. You can use all the available space around the question to do your working, however only write the answer in the answer boxes.

5. To change an answer, either rub out your original answer or put a single line through it and note down the new answer, aligning it to any answer boxes.

6. If you cannot answer a question, go on to the next question.

7. When you have completed this paper go back to any questions you have missed out and check your answers.

8. Calculators and protractors are not permitted in this test.

Good luck!

After you have finished this paper you can use the 11+ Peer Compare System™ to see how well you performed compared to others who have taken this test. You can register by visiting www.ElevenPlusExams.co.uk/FirstPastThePost to post your results anonymously and obtain the feedback.

Question 1

Jenny bought 8 litres of petrol for £8.80. She knows that 8 litres of petrol provides enough fuel to travel 40km.

a. On average, how many kilometres will 1 litre of petrol allow her to travel for?

$$\boxed{}\boxed{} \text{ km}$$

b. How much does 1 litre of petrol cost?

$$£\;\boxed{}\boxed{}.\boxed{}\boxed{}$$

c. How many litres of petrol could Jenny buy for £110.00?

$$\boxed{}\boxed{}\boxed{} \text{ l}$$

Due to an engine fault Jenny finds she can only travel $^1/_4$ of the distance she expected to.

d. If she has 40 litres of petrol in her tank, how far can she travel?

$$\boxed{}\boxed{}\boxed{} \text{ km}$$

Question 2

The table below displays the temperature of 12 different freezers.

Freezer Number	Temperature (°C)	Freezer Number	Temperature (°C)
1	-22	7	-12
2	-20	8	-24
3	-20	9	-20
4	-22	10	-18
5	-19	11	-22
6	-5	12	-20

a. Which is the coldest freezer?

Freezer Number

b. What is the difference between the temperatures of freezers 1 and 6?

°C

c. What is the mean temperature of freezers 1, 4, 7, and 10?

°C

d. If each freezer below −15°C costs £249.99, what is the total cost of these freezers?

£

Question 3

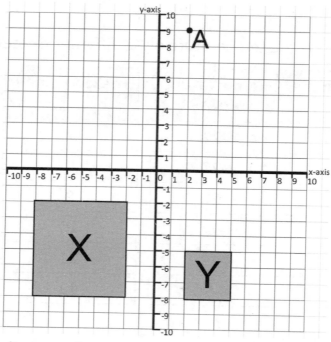

a. What are the coordinates of point A?

(3,9) ⬭   (2,8) ⬭   (2,7) ⬭   (2,9) ⬭

b. If point A is reflected in the x-axis, what are its new coordinates?

(2,9) ⬭   (-2,9) ⬭   (-3,9) ⬭   (2,-9) ⬭

c. If point A is rotated 180° about (0,0) from its original position, what would its new coordinates be?

(-9,2) ⬭   (-2,9) ⬭   (-2,-9) ⬭   (2,-9) ⬭

d. If point A is rotated 270° anti-clockwise about (0,7) from its original position, what would its new coordinates be?

(-2,9) ⬭   (-2,5) ⬭   (2,5) ⬭   (-5,-9) ⬭

e. As a percentage increase, how much greater are the side lengths of shape X than shape Y?

☐ ☐ ☐ %

Question 4

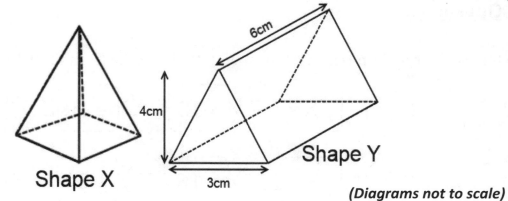

Shape X

Shape Y

4cm

6cm

3cm

(Diagrams not to scale)

a. What is the volume of shape Y?

 cm³

b. The cross-section of shape Y is an isosceles triangle. How many lines of symmetry does it have?

There are 3 times as many of shape X than of shape Y in a bag containing 20 of only these shapes.

c. How many of shape X are there in the bag?

d. What is the probability of randomly picking a shape Y?

 %

e. What is the lowest common multiple (LCM) of edges in shape X to the number of edges in shape Y?

Question 5

Below are two number machines, with their products and functions shown.

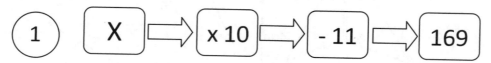

1   X ⟹ x 10 ⟹ - 11 ⟹ 169

2   Y ⟹ x 16 ⟹ + 6^2 ⟹ 196

a. What is the value of X?

b. How much greater is X than Y?

c. What is the positive square root of the output of number machine 1?

d. What is the positive square root of the output of number machine 2?

e. What is the product of the positive square roots of the outputs from number machines 1 and 2?

Numerical Reasoning
Short Test 5

Marking Grid																										Total:
Question	1					2					3					4					5					
	a	b	c	d	e	a	b	c	d	e	a	b	c	d	e	a	b	c	d	e	a	b	c	d	e	
✓ Or ×																										/22

Read the following instructions carefully:

1. You have 15 minutes to complete this test of 5 multi-part questions.
2. Work as quickly and carefully as you can.
3. When you have finished a page, go straight onto the next page until you finish the test.
4. You can use all the available space around the question to do your working, however only write the answer in the answer boxes.
5. To change an answer, either rub out your original answer or put a single line through it and note down the new answer, aligning it to any answer boxes.
6. If you cannot answer a question, go on to the next question.
7. When you have completed this paper go back to any questions you have missed out and check your answers.
8. Calculators and protractors are not permitted in this test.

Good luck!

After you have finished this paper you can use the 11+ Peer Compare System™ to see how well you performed compared to others who have taken this test. You can register by visiting www.ElevenPlusExams.co.uk/FirstPastThePost to post your results anonymously and obtain the feedback.

Question 1

Sandra and Abdul earn £300 between them per day. Sandra earns £25 more than Abdul.

a. How much does Sandra earn per day?

£ ☐☐☐ . ☐☐

b. How much does Abdul earn per day?

£ ☐☐☐ . ☐☐

Sandra spends ¼ of their combined daily earnings whilst Abdul spends 30% of it.

c. How much did Sandra spend?

£ ☐☐☐ . ☐☐

d. How much did Abdul spend?

£ ☐☐☐ . ☐☐

e. How much was left over?

£ ☐☐☐ . ☐☐

Question 2

5 identical small cubes and 1 large cube have a total mass of 5.4kg. When two small cubes are removed, the total mass falls to 4.6kg as illustrated below.

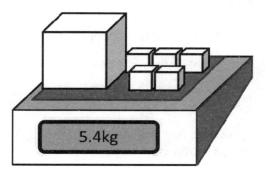 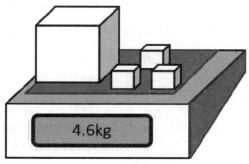

(Diagrams not to scale)

a. What is the mass of one small cube?

$$\boxed{}\boxed{}.\boxed{} \text{ kg}$$

b. What is the mass of one large cube?

$$\boxed{}\boxed{}.\boxed{} \text{ kg}$$

The volume of a large cube is 64cm³ and a small cube is 27cm³.

c. What is the length of one edge of a large cube?

$$\boxed{}\boxed{} \text{ cm}$$

d. What is the area of one face of a small cube?

$$\boxed{}\boxed{} \text{ cm}^2$$

e. What is the ratio of the area of one face of one large cube to one face of one small cube?

$$\boxed{}\boxed{} : \boxed{}$$

Question 3

Hollahade Zoo

Opening Times

13th February – 22nd July	10:00am to 5:00pm
23rd July – 30th September	9:00am to 6:00pm
1st October – 12th February	11:00am to 4:30pm

Every Friday in June and July the Zoo will close at the earlier time of 3:00pm.

a. On the 29th December, what time does Hollahade Zoo close? (Answer in 24 hour format)

$$\boxed{}\ \boxed{} : \boxed{}\ \boxed{}$$

b. On Friday 19th July, Katie arrived at 11:30am and leaves half an hour before it closes. How long does she spend at the zoo?

$$\boxed{} \text{ hour(s)} \quad \boxed{} \text{ minute(s)}$$

The number of group admissions are recorded in a particular week.

Days	Monday	Tuesday	Wednesday	Thursday	Friday
Number of group admissions	24	19	14	25	13

c. What is the mean number of group admissions in that particular week?

Question 4

An equilateral triangle, with each edge equal to 4cm, is tessellated to give the shape below.

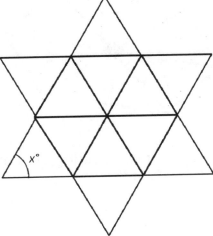

(Diagram not to scale)

a. What is the perimeter of the whole shape?

 **cm**

b. What is the size of angle $x°$?

 **°**

c. How many lines of symmetry does an equilateral triangle have?

d. If 3 of the individual triangles in the shape are to be shaded blue, what percentage of the tessellation would be shaded?

 **%**

Dylan is playing with the fair spinner below.

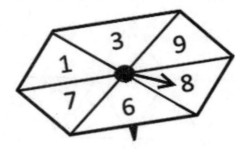

a. What is the probability of the spinner landing on a multiple of 3?

b. What is the probability of the spinner landing on a prime number?

c. What is the probability of the spinner landing on a cube number?

d. If spun twice, what is the probability that the sum of both spins add up to ten?

e. What is the order of rotational symmetry of a regular hexagon?

Numerical Reasoning
Short Test 6

Question	Marking Grid																									Total:
	1					**2**					**3**					**4**					**5**					
	a	b	c	d	e	a	b	c	d	e	a	b	c	d	e	a	b	c	d	e	a	b	c	d	e	
✓ Or ✗										▮					▮											/23

Read the following instructions carefully:

1. You have 15 minutes to complete this test of 5 multi-part questions.

2. Work as quickly and carefully as you can.

3. When you have finished a page, go straight onto the next page until you finish the test.

4. You can use all the available space around the question to do your working, however only write the answer in the answer boxes.

5. To change an answer, either rub out your original answer or put a single line through it and note down the new answer, aligning it to any answer boxes.

6. If you cannot answer a question, go on to the next question.

7. When you have completed this paper go back to any questions you have missed out and check your answers.

8. Calculators and protractors are not permitted in this test.

Good luck!

After you have finished this paper you can use the 11+ Peer Compare System™ to see how well you performed compared to others who have taken this test. You can register by visiting www.ElevenPlusExams.co.uk/FirstPastThePost to post your results anonymously and obtain the feedback.

Question 1

Michael is going on holiday to New York. He leaves home on Monday morning at 8:00am and it takes 1 hour to get to the airport. His flight departs at 11:00am and the flight's duration is 8 hours. He arrives at his hotel 2 hours after landing in New York, which is 5 hours behind London.

a. How long does Michael spend in the airport before his flight departs?

$\boxed{}\boxed{}$ **hour(s)** $\boxed{}\boxed{}$ **minute(s)**

b. When the flight departs, what time is it in New York? (Answer in 24 hour format)

$\boxed{}\boxed{}$: $\boxed{}\boxed{}$

An hour after landing in New York, Michael called his mother in London.

c. What time was it in London when he called her? (Answer in 24 hour format)

$\boxed{}\boxed{}$: $\boxed{}\boxed{}$

On his return journey, the flight time is 20% longer than the original flight.

d. How long does the return flight take?

$\boxed{}\boxed{}$. $\boxed{}\boxed{}$ **hours**

e. How long does the journey in part (d) take in minutes?

$\boxed{}\boxed{}\boxed{}$ **minutes**

Question 2

Using the compass shown below, answer the following questions.

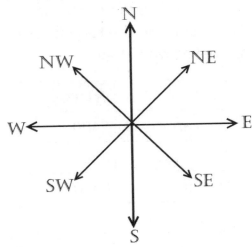

a. Mark the direction Simon is now facing if he was facing east, and then turned 90° clockwise.

N	NE	SE	S	SW	W	NW
⬭	⬭	⬭	⬭	⬭	⬭	⬭

b. Mark the direction Leah is now facing if she was facing south and then turned 270° anti-clockwise.

N	NE	SE	S	SW	W	NW
⬭	⬭	⬭	⬭	⬭	⬭	⬭

c. What is the bearing of south-west from north?

d. If Jane is currently facing north-west but turns to face east, through how many degrees clockwise has she turned?

Question 3

Adam is looking to purchase some electrical goods; he can either purchase them online for $^4/_5$ of their original price or he can purchase them in store for the original price. The shop offers a 10% discount on the total price if two items are bought in store. The costs of the items are shown below.

Item	Price
Cooker	£400
Microwave	£50
Laptop	£900
Kettle	£40

a. How much does Adam spend if he purchases the microwave and the laptop in store?

b. How much does Adam spend if he purchases the microwave and the laptop online?

c. How much does Adam save if he purchases the microwave and laptop online compared to in store?

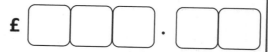

From a shop offering no discount, a company purchases 10 identical televisions with 10 aerials for a total of £4110. The aerials cost £120.

d. How much does one television cost?

Question 4

A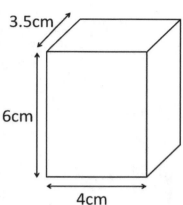

3.5cm

6cm

4cm

B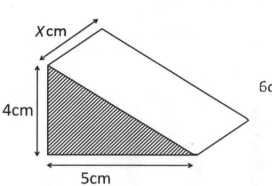

X cm

4cm

5cm

C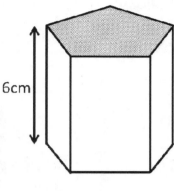

6cm

(Diagrams not to scale)

a. What is the total number of edges on shape A?

⬜⬜

b. If the shaded, cross-sectional area of shape B is 10cm², and the volume of shape B is 70cm³, what is the length of side *X*?

⬜⬜ · ⬜ **cm**

c. If the shaded, cross-sectional area of shape C is 35cm², what is its volume?

⬜⬜⬜⬜ **cm³**

d. What is the ratio of the volume of shape C to shape B?

⬜⬜ : ⬜

e. Mark below which shape has a cube number of vertices.

A   B   C

 ⬭   ⬭   ⬭

Question 5

Ryan records how long he spends revising for his exams each day during the holidays. The results are shown below.

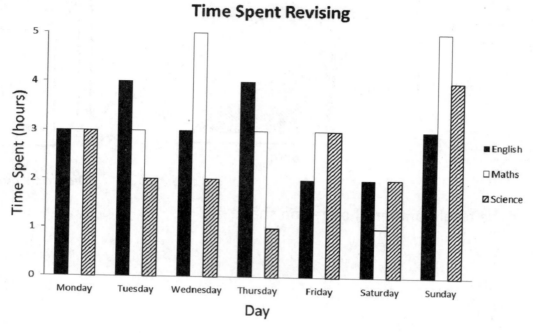

a)   How many hours did Ryan spend revising English during the holidays?

$\boxed{}\boxed{}\boxed{}$ hour(s)

b)   On average, how many hours did Ryan revise for English each day?

$\boxed{}\boxed{}$ hour(s)

c)   What is the range of time that Ryan spent revising for science ?

$\boxed{}\boxed{}$ hour(s)

d)   How much longer did Ryan revise for maths than English over the weekend?

$\boxed{}\boxed{}$ hour(s)

e)   Mark the day which represents the most hours Ryan spent revising.

Monday   Tuesday   Wednesday   Thursday   Friday   Saturday   Sunday
⬭   ⬭   ⬭   ⬭   ⬭   ⬭   ⬭

FIRST PAST THE POST® SERIES

Numerical Reasoning
Short Test 7

Question	Marking Grid																									Total:
	1					**2**					**3**					**4**					**5**					
	a	b	c	d	e	a	b	c	d	e	a	b	c	d	e	a	b	c	d	e	a	b	c	d	e	
✓ Or ✗																										/24

Read the following instructions carefully:

1. You have 15 minutes to complete this test of 5 multi-part questions.

2. Work as quickly and carefully as you can.

3. When you have finished a page, go straight onto the next page until you finish the test.

4. You can use all the available space around the question to do your working, however only write the answer in the answer boxes.

5. To change an answer, either rub out your original answer or put a single line through it and note down the new answer, aligning it to any answer boxes.

6. If you cannot answer a question, go on to the next question.

7. When you have completed this paper go back to any questions you have missed out and check your answers.

8. Calculators and protractors are not permitted in this test.

Good luck!

After you have finished this paper you can use the 11+ Peer Compare System™ to see how well you performed compared to others who have taken this test. You can register by visiting www.ElevenPlusExams.co.uk/FirstPastThePost to post your results anonymously and obtain the feedback.

Question 1

Ryan measures the diameter (in mm) of two bottle caps from two different drinks: Cap A and Cap B.

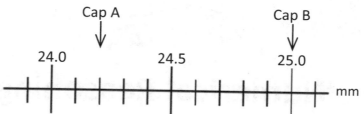

a. What is the difference between the diameters of the two bottle caps?

 **mm**

b. What percentage of Cap B's diameter is Cap A's diameter?

 **%**

c. Cap C's diameter is exactly half way on the scale between the diameters of Cap A and B's. What is Cap C's diameter?

 **mm**

Ryan places 3 blue, 5 red and 4 yellow equally sized caps in a bag.

d. What is the probability of randomly selecting a red cap?

e. What is the probability that a yellow cap is not chosen at random?

Question 2

Below is a bar chart showing the number of different language books sold at a book shop in a week.

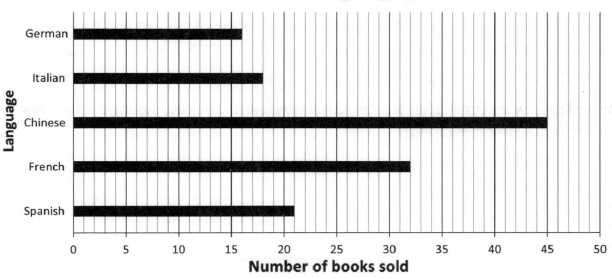

Number of different language books sold

a. How many more Chinese books were sold compared to Italian books?

[   ][   ]

b. What is the ratio of French to German books sold?

[   ][   ] : [   ]

c. What is the ratio of Spanish to Italian books sold?

[   ][   ] : [   ]

d. Mark the modal language of books sold.

Spanish	French	Chinese	Italian
⬭	⬭	⬭	⬭

e. If Spanish book sales increased by $^1/_3$, what would be the new number sold?

[   ][   ] **books**

Question 3

Simon swims 6 lengths of a swimming pool per day for *x* days. Jade swims 5 more lengths per day than Simon for *y* days.

a. Mark the expression for the combined number of laps swam by Simon and Jade.

$6x + 5y$ $6y + 11x$ $6x + 11y$ $6y + 5x$

b. If Jade swam for 6 days and the total number of lengths swam is 114, how many days did Simon swim for?

 **days**

A diagram of the swimming pool is shown below.

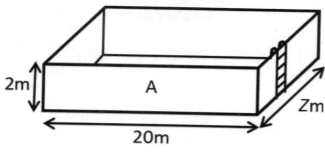

(Diagram not to scale)

c. What is the surface area of face A?

 **m²**

d. If the total capacity of the pool is 360m³ when filled to the top, what is the value of *Z*?

 **m**

e. How many lines of symmetry does face A have?

Question 4

The first four terms of a sequence are shown below.

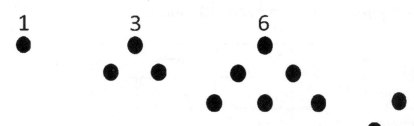

a. What is the sum of the fifth and sixth terms of this sequence?

b. What is the lowest common multiple (LCM) of the fourth and fifth term?

c. Convert the third term of the sequence into Roman numerals.

d. Mark below the name given to these types of numbers.

Triangular	Consecutive	Cube	Square
⬭	⬭	⬭	⬭

e. Of the first four terms, how many are prime numbers?

Question 5

The table below shows a partly completed train timetable. It takes 20 minutes to travel between any 2 stations. Trains run every 40 minutes from Harkend to Redmond.

Stop	Time		
Harkend	11:20	?	12:40
Grenham Central	11:40	?	?
Scottwood	12:00	12:40	?
Hayes	12:20	13:00	?
Redmond	12:40	?	?

Jack travels to work from Grenham Central to Redmond. He arrives at Grenham Central at 12:25.

a. How long does Jack have to wait for the next train?

◻◻ **minutes**

b. What time does Jack arrive at Redmond?

◻◻ : ◻◻ **pm**

c. On a particular day, the journey between Harkend and Redmond from 11:20 takes 50% longer than usual. What is the total journey time on this day?

◻◻ **hour(s)** ◻◻ **minute(s)**

d. If train fares cost £3.20 per adult and £2.30 per child, what is the cost for 3 adults and 2 children?

£ ◻◻ . ◻◻

FIRST PAST THE POST® SERIES

Numerical Reasoning
Short Test 8

Read the following instructions carefully:

1. You have 15 minutes to complete this test of 5 multi-part questions.

2. Work as quickly and carefully as you can.

3. When you have finished a page, go straight onto the next page until you finish the test.

4. You can use all the available space around the question to do your working, however only write the answer in the answer boxes.

5. To change an answer, either rub out your original answer or put a single line through it and note down the new answer, aligning it to any answer boxes.

6. If you cannot answer a question, go on to the next question.

7. When you have completed this paper go back to any questions you have missed out and check your answers.

8. Calculators and protractors are not permitted in this test.

Good luck!

After you have finished this paper you can use the 11+ Peer Compare System[TM] to see how well you performed compared to others who have taken this test. You can register by visiting www.ElevenPlusExams.co.uk/FirstPastThePost to post your results anonymously and obtain the feedback.

Question 1

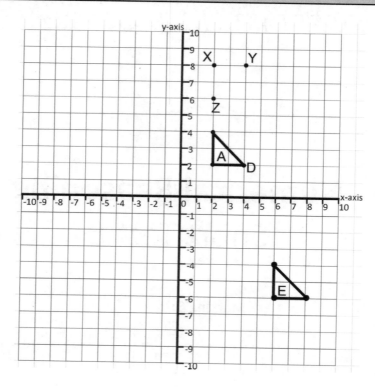

a. If shape A is rotated 180° clockwise about (0,0) to give shape B, mark the new coordinates of D for shape B.

   (-4,2) ⬭   (-2,4) ⬭   (4,-2) ⬭   (-4,-2) ⬭

b. If shape A is reflected in the y-axis to give shape C, mark the new coordinates of D for shape C.

   (-4,2) ⬭   (-2,9) ⬭   (-4,9) ⬭   (2,-9) ⬭

c. If points X, Y and Z are three corners of a square, mark the coordinates of the fourth corner.

   (3,6) ⬭   (4,6) ⬭   (6,3) ⬭   (6,4) ⬭

d. If shape A is translated to give shape E, mark below the description of this translation.

   6 down, 3 right ⬭   6 up, 5 right ⬭   8 down, 4 right ⬭   7 down, 6 right ⬭

Question 2

The diagram shows the design of a garden.

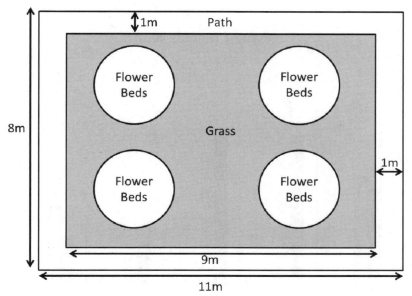

(Diagram not to scale)

a. What is the perimeter of the outside of the path?

 **m**

b. If the combined area of the 4 flower beds is 26m², what is the area of one flower bed?

 **m²**

c. Given that the paths are 1m wide, what is the area of the grass and the flower beds?

 **m²**

d. What is the area of the grass part alone?

 **m²**

e. What is the ratio of the area of grass to the area of the flower beds?

Question 3

The graph below shows the number of medals won by different countries in the London Olympics.

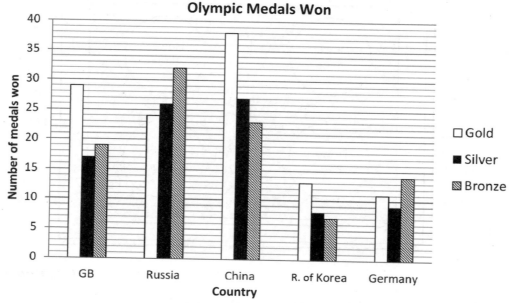

a. What is the median number of bronze medals won?

b. What is the mean number of silver medals won by these countries?

c. If Hungary won $\frac{1}{6}$ of the number of gold medals won by Russia, how many gold medals did Hungary win?

d. What is the highest common factor (HCF) of the number of gold and bronze medals won by Russia?

e. What is the lowest common multiple (LCM) of the number of silver and bronze medals won by the Republic of Korea?

Question 4

A pinball is released at point A, and then deflected at point B before coming to a rest at point C.

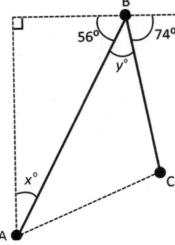

(Diagram not to scale)

a. What is the sum of the interior angles in a triangle?

b. What is the size of angle $x°$?

c. If lines AC and BC are of equal length, mark the type of triangle formed by ABC.

Right Angled   Isosceles   Scalene   Equilateral

d. How many lines of symmetry does the triangle ABC have?

e. What is the size of angle $y°$?

Question 5

Below are three number machines. Their inputs are unknown but all operations and outputs are given.

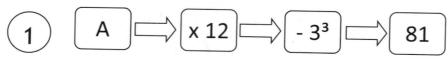

(1)　A $\Rightarrow$ x 12 $\Rightarrow$ - 3³ $\Rightarrow$ 81

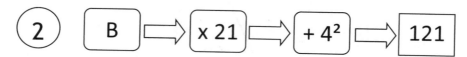

(2)　B $\Rightarrow$ x 21 $\Rightarrow$ + 4² $\Rightarrow$ 121

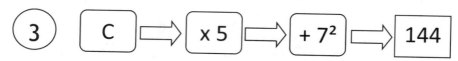

(3)　C $\Rightarrow$ x 5 $\Rightarrow$ + 7² $\Rightarrow$ 144

a. What is the input for number machine 1?

b. What is the positive square root of the output from number machine 3?

c. What is the product of the inputs from number machines 1 and 2?

d. What is the output from number machine 3 less the output from number machine 1?

e. What is the lowest common multiple (LCM) of the inputs for number machines 1 and 2?

Numerical Reasoning
Short Test 9

Question	Marking Grid																									Total:
	1					**2**					**3**					**4**					**5**					
	a	b	c	d	e	a	b	c	d	e	a	b	c	d	e	a	b	c	d	e	a	b	c	d	e	
✓ Or ✗																										/25

Read the following instructions carefully:

1. You have 15 minutes to complete this test of 5 multi-part questions.

2. Work as quickly and carefully as you can.

3. When you have finished a page, go straight onto the next page until you finish the test.

4. You can use all the available space around the question to do your working, however only write the answer in the answer boxes.

5. To change an answer, either rub out your original answer or put a single line through it and note down the new answer, aligning it to any answer boxes.

6. If you cannot answer a question, go on to the next question.

7. When you have completed this paper go back to any questions you have missed out and check your answers.

8. Calculators and protractors are not permitted in this test.

Good luck!

After you have finished this paper you can use the <u>11+ Peer Compare System</u>™ to see how well you performed compared to others who have taken this test. You can register by visiting <u>www.ElevenPlusExams.co.uk/FirstPastThePost</u> to post your results anonymously and obtain the feedback.

Question 1

The pie chart below shows the favourite colours of 720 children.

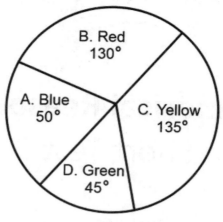

(Diagram not to scale)

a. How many children said red was their favourite colour?

b. How many more children preferred the colour red to green?

c. What is the ratio of children who preferred blue to green?

d. Mark the letter for the colour that $^1/_8$ of the children said was their favourite.

       A   B   C   D

e. If 15% of all the children selected hockey as their favourite sport, how many children is this?

Question 2

A   B   C   D   E

(Diagrams not to scale)

a. Which shape has more than 4 lines of symmetry?

b. What is the order of rotational symmetry of shape D?

c. Which 2 shapes have an equal number of lines of symmetry?

☐ and ☐

d. What is the size of an interior angle in shape A?

☐☐☐ °

e. What is the size of angle *x*° in shape D?

☐☐☐ °

Question 3

On a particular day, the temperature is recorded and shown on the diagram below.

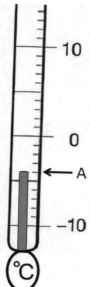

a. What is the value of A?

 °C

b. If the temperature increases by 7.6°C, what is the new temperature?

 °C

Bruce checks the minimum temperatures for the week. His findings are below:

8°C   0°C   -6°C   -5°C   -3°C   -1°C   0°C

c. What is the mean minimum temperature across the week?

 °C

d. What is the range of temperatures for the week?

 °C

e. What is the difference between the median and modal temperatures for the week?

 °C

Question 4

Below is a random selection of numbered cards.

| 1 | 9 | 3 | 6 | 7 | 8 | 11 | 27 |

a. What is the probability of choosing a card that is a cube number?

$$\frac{\square}{\square}$$

b. What is the probability of choosing a card that is a triangular number?

$$\frac{\square}{\square}$$

c. Four cards are selected to make the number 6918. What is the value of the 9?

☐ ☐ ☐ ☐

d. In its simplest form, what is the ratio of even to odd numbers?

☐ : ☐

e. How many of the cards are prime numbers?

☐

Question 5

Sophie is looking at time differences of different cities relative to London.

Destination	Time difference relative to London (hours)
Hong Kong	+ 7
Los Angeles	-8
Brussels	+1
Sydney	+9
Boston	?

a. What time is it in London when it is 9:00am in Los Angeles? (Answer in 24 hour format)

⬜⬜ : ⬜⬜

b. If Sophie departs from London at 8:50pm, and it takes 1 hour to travel to Brussels, what time is it in Brussels when Sophie lands?

⬜⬜ : ⬜⬜ **pm**

c. Convert the answer in part (b) into 24 hour format.

⬜⬜ : ⬜⬜

d. If the time in Boston is 4:23am when it is 9:23am in London, how many hours behind London is Boston?

⬜

Sophie, who is 12 years old, travels to Brussels with her mother and father. Flight tickets cost £250 for adults and £199 for children.

e. What is the total cost of their tickets?

£ ⬜⬜⬜⬜ . ⬜⬜

FIRST PAST THE POST® SERIES

Numerical Reasoning
Short Test 10

Question	Marking Grid																									Total:
	1					**2**					**3**					**4**					**5**					
	a	b	c	d	e	a	b	c	d	e	a	b	c	d	e	a	b	c	d	e	a	b	c	d	e	
✓ Or ✗																										/25

Read the following instructions carefully:

1. You have 15 minutes to complete this test of 5 multi-part questions.

2. Work as quickly and carefully as you can.

3. When you have finished a page, go straight onto the next page until you finish the test.

4. You can use all the available space around the question to do your working, however only write the answer in the answer boxes.

5. To change an answer, either rub out your original answer or put a single line through it and note down the new answer, aligning it to any answer boxes.

6. If you cannot answer a question, go on to the next question.

7. When you have completed this paper go back to any questions you have missed out and check your answers.

8. Calculators and protractors are not permitted in this test.

Good luck!

After you have finished this paper you can use the 11+ Peer Compare System™ to see how well you performed compared to others who have taken this test. You can register by visiting www.ElevenPlusExams.co.uk/FirstPastThePost to post your results anonymously and obtain the feedback.

Question 1

The following questions are based on the number sequences below.

Sequence A	6,	11,	16,	21,	26
Sequence B	3,	6,	12,	24,	48
Sequence C	243,	81,	27,	9,	3

a. By how much does each term in sequence A increase to give the following term?

b. How many triangular numbers are present in the terms given in sequence B?

c. What is the next term in sequence B?

d. What is the range of the terms given in sequence B?

e. What is the next term in sequence C?

Question 2

The diagram below shows a trough of water used by animals on a farm. The cross-sectional, shaded area is 800cm², and the length of the trough is *X*m long.

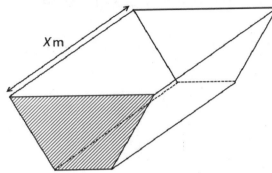

(Diagram not to scale)

a. If the maximum capacity of the water trough is 160,000cm³, what is the value of *X* in cm?

 **cm**

b. If one pig requires 5000cm³ of water per day, for how many pigs is there sufficient water in a full trough?

c. If one horse requires 40,000cm³ of water per day, for how many days is there enough water in a full trough?

d. The farmer has 5 identical troughs to the one shown in the diagram above. What is the total volume of water he can fill up the troughs with?

 **cm³**

e. If each trough costs £538.75, what is the total cost of all 5 troughs?

£ ☐☐☐☐☐ . ☐☐

Question 3

For five consecutive days, Jason bought 3 strawberry sweets and 2 orange sweets, whilst Bryan bought 4 lemon sweets and 1 orange sweet.

a. What is the total number of sweets Jason and Bryan bought over the five days?

☐☐☐

b. What fraction of the overall sweets they bought are lemon flavoured?

$\frac{\Box}{\Box}$

c. If the children collect the sweets they bought in a bag and choose 1 randomly, what is the likelihood of it being orange flavoured?

☐☐☐ %

d. What is the ratio of strawberry to lemon sweets purchased by the boys?

☐ : ☐

e. If the children remove all of the lemon sweets, what is the probability of a randomly selected sweet being strawberry flavoured?

☐☐☐ %

Question 4

The scale on the right shows 15 spheres of equal mass on a weighing scale.

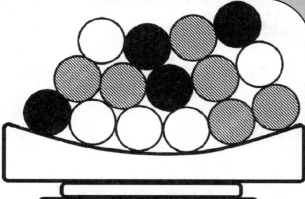

a. What is the total mass of the spheres on the scale? (in g)

 g

b. How much does each sphere weigh?

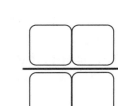 g

c. What fraction of spheres are black?

d. When a cube is added to the scale, the total mass increases to 9.8kg. How much does this cube weigh?

 g

e. What is the ratio of black to grey to white spheres?

☐ : ☐ : ☐

Question 5

a. If Jude is 150cm tall, approximately how many feet tall is he?

☐☐ **feet**

b. If Ryan is $^{13}/_{30}$ of Jude's height, how tall is Ryan?

☐☐☐ · ☐ **cm**

c. If Jude's mother is five sixths of Jude's height, how tall is she?

☐☐☐ · ☐ **cm**

d. The ratio of William's height to Jude's height is 6:5. How tall is William?

☐☐☐ · ☐ **cm**

e. An equation to calculate Maria's height (m) in centimetres from Jude's height (j) in centimetres is shown below. Using this equation, how tall is Maria?

$$m = 0.75j + 20$$

☐☐☐ · ☐ **cm**

FIRST PAST THE POST® SERIES

Multi-Part Numerical Reasoning
Book 1
Short Tests 1-10

Answers and Explanations

As you complete each short test, remember that you can use the 11+ Peer Compare System™ to see how well you performed in comparison to others who have taken this test.

You can register by visiting www.ElevenPlusExams.co.uk/ FirstPastThePost to post your results anonymously and obtain the feedback.

Your unique 16 digit access code is:

PY5W-T13T-ZWSI-7O23

Short Test 1 Answers and Explanations

Question	Answer	Explanation
1 a	2 and $^1/_3$ hours	A mixed fraction is a mixture of a whole number and a fraction. Recognise there are 60 minutes in an hour, simplify $^{20}/_{60}$ (to $^1/_3$) then add 2 hours.
1 b	1 and $^5/_6$ hours	A mixed fraction is a mixture of a whole number and a fraction. Recognise there are 60 minutes in an hour, simplify $^{50}/_{60}$ (to $^5/_6$) then add 1 hour.
1 c	250 minutes	Convert the times into minutes (140 and 110) then find the sum of 140 + 110 = 250 minutes.
1 d	44%	Convert the length of time into minutes. As a percentage of 250 minutes, 110 minutes is $^{11}/_{25}$ = 44%.
1 e	4 and $^1/_6$ hours	Add 2 and $^1/_3$ and 1 and $^5/_6$. Alternatively, convert 250 minutes into a mixed fraction, which is 4 and $^1/_6$ hours.
2 a	B	7 units, 9 tenths and 6 hundredths can be written as 7.96. Identify which numbers could be the closest to 7.96 and work out the differences. 8.14109 (B) is clearly the nearest value.
2 b	51.75	Addition of E and B first, as they are in brackets (15), followed by the multiplication of A, which gives 15 x 3.45 = 51.75.
2 c	49	Addition of C and D first, as they are in brackets (7), and then apply the index which is 2 giving 7^2= 49.
2 d	C	Options A and C are closest to 4. The difference between C and 4 is smaller than A and 4. A: 4 - 3.45 = 0.55 whereas C: 4.50521 - 4 = 0.50521.
3 a	$f = 8b - 4$	The grandfather's age (f) is 4 years less than 8 times Ben's age (b), giving the equation $f = 8b - 4$.
3 b	60 years	Substitute 8 for b to give (8 x 8) - 4 = 60 years old.
3 c	62 years	If Ben's age has increased by 2 years, his grandfather's age will have also increased by 2 years.
3 d	12 years	Substitute 63 for m and rearrange the equation to give (63 - 3) ÷ 5 = b, where b is 12.
4 a	7.00cm	Recognise opposite sides of a rectangle are equal in length. Therefore y is the same as the value opposite (7.00cm).
4 b	23.00cm	Recognise that opposite sides of a rectangle are equal in length. Therefore the perimeter is (9.5 x 2) + (2 x 2) = 23.00cm.
4 c	C	The area for shape C is 90.25cm² which is larger than the other areas (shape B's area is 19cm²).
4 d	C and D	The area for shape C is 90.25cm² and the area for shape D is 90cm².
4 e	6.00cm	The formula for the area of a parallelogram is base length x height. By rearranging the equation, 90 ÷ 15 = 6 is the expression needed to find the length x.
5 a	150 minutes	The longest time is 2 hours and 30 minutes which is 2 ½ hours. There are 60 minutes in an hour, so convert this value into minutes (2.5 x 60 = 150) giving 150 minutes.
5 b	1 hour 45 minutes	The range of a set of numbers is the difference between the smallest and largest number. The largest number is 150 minutes and the smallest number is 45 minutes so the range is 105 minutes or 1 hour 45 minutes (150 - 45 = 105).
5 c	1 hour 40 minutes	The median is the middle number when numbers are put in order of size. The middle number in this set is 1 hour and 40 minutes.
5 d	1 hour 42 minutes	The mean is found by adding all the numbers in a set and dividing by how many numbers there are in the set. The sum of time spent revising is 510 which is across 5 days. The mean is therefore 510 ÷ 5 = 102 minutes which is equivalent to 1 hour and 42 minutes.

Short Test 2 Answers and Explanations

Question	Answer	Explanation
1 a	$12x + 6y$	There are 12 boxes with x blue pencils and 6 boxes with y red pencils, giving the equation $12x + 6y$.
1 b	$5x + 6y$	7 boxes of x pencils are taken away from the original amount of 12 boxes. Hence 5 boxes of x pencils remain.
1 c	$5x + 3y$	½ of $6x$ equals $3x$, giving the new expression $5x + 3y$.
1 d	91	Substitute $x=3$ and $y=5$ into the expression, to give $(2 \times 3) + (5 \times 5) + (4 \times 3 \times 5) = 91$.
2 a	£7.20	Subtract £112.80 from £120 to give £7.20.
2 b	£3.60	Divide £7.20 by 2 to give £3.60.
2 c	£75.00	Divide £525 by 7 days to give £75.00 per day.
2 d	£45.00	Find 20% of £75 which is £15, followed by the product of £15 and 3 days which gives £45.00.
3 a	750ml	The beaker is filled with water up to 750ml.
3 b	375ml	Finding ½ of 750ml which gives 375ml.
3 c	1.25l	The beaker is full at 1250ml. Converting into litres requires dividing by 1000.
3 d	937.50ml	25% of 750ml is 187.5ml. This value added to 750ml gives 937.50ml.
4 a	7	Convert 2.1 metres into centimetres to give 210cm. To find the number of paving stones, divide $210 \div 30$ which is 7.
4 b	11	Convert 3.3 metres into centimetres to give 330cm. Dividing 330 by 30 to find the number of paving stones $(330 \div 30)$ which gives 11.
4 c	$6.93m^2$	The area of a rectangle is length x width. Therefore find the product of 2.1m x 3.3m = $6.93m^2$.
4 d	77	Multiply the number of stones that fit along the width by the height $(7 \times 11 = 77)$.
5 a	165	The number of pigeons is the total number of birds (186) minus the number of robins and gulls $(6 + 15 = 21)$ resulting in $(186 - 21)$ 165.
5 b	124	If twice as many flew south, then the ratio of south to north is 2:1. The sum required is $(186 \div 3) \times 2 = 124$.
5 c	62	The total number of birds divided by the number of hours is $186 \div 3$ giving 62.
5 d	5:2	The ratio of gulls to robins is 15:6. Simplifying this gives 5:2, as both numbers are factors of 3.

Short Test 3 Answers and Explanations

Question	Answer	Explanation
1 a	540 seconds	The journey takes 9 minutes. Multiply 9 by 60 to convert into seconds (540 seconds).
1 b	Preston Road to Preston Hill	The difference between Preston Road to Preston Hill is 13 minutes which is shorter than the difference between Wembley Park and Preston Road which is 22 minutes.
1 c	Thursday	The journey on Thursday is 13 minutes and on Saturday it is 18 minutes.
1 d	1080 seconds	A 20% increase on 15 minutes is 18 minutes. Multiply 18 minutes by 60 seconds to give 1080 seconds.
2 a	96	The following term is double the previous term in this sequence. Hence B is 48 x 2 = 96.
2 b	288	Term C is double term B which gives 192. Addition of 192 and 96 gives 288.
2 c	1.5	The value of term A is ½ of 3 (= 1.5).
2 d	3	12, 24 and 48 are all multiples of 4, 3 and 6 are not exactly divisible by 4. Therefore 3 numbers are multiples of 4.
2 e	2	3 and 6 are the only triangular numbers in the sequence. 12, 24, and 48 are not triangular numbers as they cannot be arranged as a triangle using, for example, dots.
3 a	15.00%	For the percentage who said maths, find 100% - 42(drama) - 20(English) - 23(P.E.) = 15.00%.
3 b	40	20% of students chose English, therefore find 20% of 200 = 40.
3 c	15	Finding $\frac{3}{8}$ of 40 = 15.
3 d	25	Finding $\frac{5}{8}$ of 40 = 25 or 40 Students - 15 Girls = 15 Boys.
3 e	72°	20% of students chose English. Find 20% of 360° = 72°.
4 a	£10.00	$\frac{2}{3}$ of the savings each week are put towards the bike. Find $\frac{2}{3}$ of £15 = £10.00.
4 b	£20.00	$\frac{1}{3}$ of the savings each week are given to charity. Find $\frac{1}{3}$ of £15 = £5, and then multiply by 4 which equals £20.00.
4 c	11	Every week, Adrian puts £5 towards charity. Find 55 ÷ 5 (for the number of weeks) which equals 11 weeks.
4 d	75%	After 9 weeks, Adrian will have saved £90 towards the bike (£10 x 9). The percentage of $\frac{90}{120}$ is 75%.
4 e	£50.00	If the bike costs £100, he needs to save for 10 weeks (100 ÷ 10 = 10). He donated £5 a week to charity, so has donated 10 x 5 = £50.00 after 10 weeks.
5 a	3	On a Venn diagram, the intersection of the overlapping circles shows data belonging to both groups. Therefore the value required for children who own both dogs and fish is 3.
5 b	15	On a Venn diagram, the area outside the circles but within the rectangle represents data that do not belong to any of the categories. This value is 15.
5 c	$\frac{3}{8}$	The number of children who own fish is 12 + 3 = 15. The total number of children is 40, so the fraction needed is $\frac{15}{40}$ which simplifies to $\frac{3}{8}$.
5 d	5:6	The values in the intersection should not be included. The ratio of only dogs owned to only fish owned is 10:12 which simplifies to 5:6.
5 e	16	Find 20% of the people who own neither dogs nor fish, which is 3, then add to the 13 already existing dog owners giving a total of 16 owners.

Short Test 4 Answers and Explanations

Question	Answer	Explanation
1 a	**5km**	8 litres provides fuel to travel 40km, so 1 litre will provide 5km of fuel (40 ÷ 8 = 5).
1 b	**£1.10**	8 litres costs £8.80, so 1 litre will cost £1.10 (8.80 ÷ 8 = 1.10).
1 c	**100l**	If one litre costs £1.10, £110.00 will give 100 litres of petrol (110 ÷ 1.10 = 100).
1 d	**50km**	40 litres of petrol will normally provide sufficient fuel for 200km (40 x 5 = 200). With the engine fault she can travel ¼ of this distance, 50km (200 x ¼ = 50).
2 a	**Freezer Number 8**	The temperature that is the most negative is -24°C, which corresponds to freezer number 8.
2 b	**17°C**	The difference between -22°C and -5°C is 17°C.
2 c	**-18.50°C**	Find the sum of (-22 + -22 + -12 + -18) to get -74 and then divide by 4 to find the mean that is -18.50°C.
2 d	**£2499.90**	The total number of freezers below -15°C is 10. Multiply 10 by the cost of each freezer, £249.99, giving a total of £2499.90.
3 a	**(2,9)**	The point A is 2 squares to the right, and 9 squares up which gives the coordinates (2,9).
3 b	**(2,-9)**	Reflect in the x-axis (the horizontal line passing through (0,0)) to find the new coordinates of (2,-9).
3 c	**(-2,-9)**	A rotation of 180° about (0,0) gives the point (-2,-9) with both of the x and y values being negative.
3 d	**(2,5)**	Rotating 270° anticlockwise about (0,7) gives the point (2,5). Rotating 270° anticlockwise has the same effect as rotating 90° clockwise.
3 e	**100%**	The length of one side of X is 6 units and the length of one side of Y is 3 units. As X is double the value of Y, the percentage increase is 100%.
4 a	**36cm³**	The volume of a 3D shape = cross-sectional area x length. The volume is (3 x 4) ÷ 2 for the cross-sectional area, multiplied by the length, which is 6, giving a volume of 36cm³.
4 b	**1**	An isosceles triangle has one line of symmetry.
4 c	**15**	There is a 3:1 ratio of shape X to shape Y. The number of shape X blocks is therefore (20 ÷ 4) x 3 = 15.
4 d	**25%**	The probability of picking a shape Y block is 5/20 (=¼) which, when converted into a percentage gives 25%.
4 e	**72**	The number of edges in shape X is 8 and for shape Y is 9. The LCM is therefore 72.
5 a	**18**	Using the output 169, work backwards to give the sum (169 + 11) ÷ 10 = 18.
5 b	**8**	The input for Y is (196 - 6²) ÷ 16 = 10. The difference between the input for X (i.e. 18) and the input for Y (i.e. 10) is 8.
5 c	**13**	A square root of a number is the number you multiply by itself to make that number. The positive square root of 169 is 13.
5 d	**14**	A square root of a number is the number you multiply by itself to make that number. The positive square root of 196 is 14.
5 e	**182**	The positive square roots of the outputs from number machines 1 and 2 are 13 and 14. The product of 13 and 14 is 182.

Short Test 5 Answers and Explanations

Question	Answer	Explanation
1 a	**£162.50**	If Sandra earns £25 more than Abdul, she earns (£300 ÷ 2) + (£25 ÷ 2) = £150 + £12.50 = £162.50.
1 b	**£137.50**	If Abdul earns £25 less than Sandra, he earns (£300 ÷ 2) - (£25 ÷ 2) = £150 - £12.50 = £137.50.
1 c	**£75.00**	Sandra spends ¼ of £300 which is £300 ÷ 4 = £75.00.
1 d	**£90.00**	Abdul spends 30% of £300 which is £300 ÷ 10 x 3 = £90.00.
1 e	**£135.00**	The amount left over is £90.00 + £75.00 taken away from £300.00 which gives £135.00.
2 a	**0.4kg**	There are 2 more small cubes on the scale reading 5.4kg. 2 small cubes have a mass of 0.8kg (5.4 - 4.6 = 0.8). One small cube is ½ of 0.8kg which is 0.4kg.
2 b	**3.4kg**	The mass of one small cube is 0.4kg. The mass of three small cubes is 1.2kg. Therefore the mass of the large cube is 3.4kg (4.6 - 1.2 = 3.4).
2 c	**4cm**	If the volume of a cube is 64cm³, the length of one edge is the cube root of 64cm³ = 4cm.
2 d	**9cm²**	The cube root of 27cm³ is 3cm, and then the area of one side is 3cm x 3cm which equals 9cm².
2 e	**16:9**	The surface area of one side of a large cube is 16cm² and the surface area of one side of the small cube is 9cm². The ratio between them is 16:9, which can not be simplified any further.
3 a	**16:30**	The 29th December falls in the '1st October - 12th February' category, so it closes at 4:30pm which is 16:30 in 24 hour format.
3 b	**3 hours 00 minutes**	If the zoo closes at 3:00pm and she leaves at 2:30pm, she spent 3 hours at the zoo. 14:30 - 11:30 = 3 hours.
3 c	**19**	The sum of the number of group admissions is 95 and the number of days is 5.
4 a	**48cm**	The total distance around the edge of the shape is each length (4cm) multiplied by the number of edges (12) which gives 48cm (12 x 4 = 48).
4 b	**60⁰**	The sum of all of the interior angles in a triangle is 180⁰. In an equilateral triangle, all interior angles are equal so the size of x is 180⁰ ÷ 3 = 60⁰.
4 c	**3**	A shape has symmetry when it can be divided into two equal, mirror images. An equilateral triangle has 3 lines of symmetry.
4 d	**25%**	The total number of triangles is 12, so the fraction of blue triangles is $^3/_{12}$ which is equivalent to 25%.
5 a	$^1/_2$	A multiple of a number is the result when it is multiplied by another number. $^3/_6$ of the options are multiples of 3 (3, 6 and 9) which simplifies to ½.
5 b	$^1/_3$	A prime number is a number that has only two factors; one and the number itself. The prime numbers are 3 and 7, so the probability of the spinner landing on one is $^2/_6$ which simplifies to $^1/_3$.
5 c	$^1/_3$	A cube number is the product of a number that is multiplied by itself twice (e.g. 2 x 2 x 2 = 8). The two cube numbers on the spinner are 1 and 8, so the probability is $^2/_6$ which simplifies to $^1/_3$.
5 d	$^1/_9$	The number of possible combinations is 36, and there are 4 ways of finding the sum of 10 (7 and 3, 3 and 7, 9 and 1, 1 and 9) so the fraction required is $^4/_{36}$ which simplifies to $^1/_9$.
5 e	**6**	Rotational symmetry is when you turn a shape around its centre to see how often it maps onto itself. A hexagon has a rotational symmetry of 6.

Short Test 6 Answers and Explanations

Question	Answer	Explanation
1 a	**2 hours 00 minutes**	If he reaches the airport at 9:00am and his flight departs at 11:00am, he spends 2 hours at the airport.
1 b	**06:00**	If New York is 5 hours behind London, 11:00 minus 5 hours is 06:00 in 24 hour format.
1 c	**20:00**	He made the call 9 hours after his departure from London, so 9 hours after 11:00 is 20:00 in 24 hour format.
1 d	**9.60 hours**	Find 20% of 8 hours (the original flight duration) which is 1.6 hours, then add 1.6 hours to 8 hours to give a total journey duration of 9.60 hours.
1 e	**576 minutes**	There are 60 minutes in an hour. Convert 9 hours into minutes (9 x 60 = 540) and convert separately 0.6 hours into minutes (0.6 x 60 = 36). Add 540 and 36 together for the total journey duration which gives 576 minutes.
2 a	**S**	90° is a ¼ of a turn of a full circle. If he turns 90° clockwise, he will now be facing south (S).
2 b	**W**	She turns ¾ of a circle anticlockwise so she is now facing west (W).
2 c	**225°**	A bearing is the clockwise angle between north and the direction in which something has travelled to. Therefore the bearing of south-west from north is 225°.
2 d	**135°**	There are 360° degrees in a full circle. Turning clockwise from north-west to east is $^3/_8$ of 360° which is 135°.
3 a	**£855.00**	Find 10% of the total £950 which is £95, and then subtract £95 from £950 to give £855.00.
3 b	**£760.00**	Find $^4/_5$ of the total £950 which is £760.00.
3 c	**£95.00**	If he purchases it in store, he spends £855. If he purchases it online, he spends £760. He saves £855 - £760 = £95.00 buying it online.
3 d	**£399.00**	The cost of 10 televisions is £4110 - £120 (aerials) = £3990. The price of 1 television is £3990 ÷ 10 = £399.00.
4 a	**12**	Shape A is a cuboid and has 12 edges.
4 b	**7.0cm**	If the cross-sectional area is 10cm² and the volume is 70cm³, the length X is 70 ÷ 10 = 7.0cm.
4 c	**210cm³**	If the cross-sectional area is 35cm², and the length of the shape is 6cm, the volume of the shape is 35 x 6 = 210cm³.
4 d	**3:1**	The volume of shape C is 210cm³ and the volume of shape B is 70cm³. The ratio is 210:70 which simplifies to 3:1.
4 e	**A**	Shape A has 8 vertices, shape B has 6 vertices and shape C has 10 vertices. Of those options, 8 is the only cube number (since 8 = 2 x 2 x 2).
5 a	**21 hours**	The sum of hours spent revising English is 21 (3 + 4 + 3 + 4 + 2 + 2 + 3 = 21).
5 b	**3 hours**	The sum of hours spend revising English was 21. Divide this by the number of days in a week (7) which gives 3 hours of revision per day (21 hours ÷ 7 days = 3 hours per day).
5 c	**3 hours**	The longest number of hours spent revising science was 4 hours and the shortest was 1 hour, so the range is 3 hours (4 - 1 = 3).
5 d	**1 hour**	Ryan spent 6 hours revising maths and 5 hours revising English. Therefore Ryan spent 1 hour longer revising maths than English (6 - 5 = 1).
5 e	**Sunday**	Ryan spent a total of 12 hours revising on Sunday (3 + 4 + 5 = 12), all of the histogram bars combined here are noticeably the tallest.

Short Test 7 Answers and Explanations

Question	Answer	Explanation
1 a	0.80mm	Cap A's diameter is 24.2mm and Cap B's diameter is 25.0mm. The difference in diameters is 25.0 - 24.2 = 0.80mm.
1 b	96.80%	Cap A's diameter is 24.2mm and Cap B's diameter is 25.0mm. From the fraction 24.2 ÷ 25.0, multiply both sides of the fraction by 4 to give 96.8 ÷ 100 which is also 96.80%.
1 c	24.60mm	The middle value between 24.2mm and 25.0mm is 24.60mm.
1 d	$^5/_{12}$	The total number of caps is 12 and the number of red caps is 5. The probability of choosing a red cap is $^5/_{12}$.
1 e	$^2/_3$	The number of red and blue caps is 8 and the total number of caps is 12. Therefore the probability is $^8/_{12}$ which simplifies to $^2/_3$.
2 a	27	The number of Chinese books and Italian books sold were 45 and 18 respectively. The difference is 45 - 18 = 27.
2 b	2:1	The number of French and German books sold were 32 and 16 respectively. The ratio is 32:16 which simplifies to 2:1.
2 c	7:6	The number of Spanish and Italian books sold were 21 and 18 respectively. The ratio is 21:18 which simplifies to 7:6.
2 d	Chinese	The mode is the number in a set that occurs most often. More Chinese books were sold than any other language, so the modal book sold is Chinese.
2 e	28	Find a $^1/_3$ of 21, which is 7, then add it to 21 to get 28.
3 a	$6x + 11y$	Simon swims 6 lengths for x number of days ($6x$) and Jade swims 5 more lengths than Simon for y number of days ($11y$) giving the expression $6x + 11y$ for the total lengths swam.
3 b	8 days	Substitute 6 for y and make the expression equal to 114. This gives $6x + (11 \times 6) = 114$. Rearranging this gives $6x = 48$, and solving for x gives $x = 8$.
3 c	40m²	The area of a rectangle is the width multiplied by the height which is 20m x 2m = 40m².
3 d	9m	If the surface area of face A is 40m² and the total volume is 360m³, the length of Z is 360 ÷ 40 = 9m.
3 e	2	A shape has symmetry if it can be divided into 2 equal, mirror images. A rectangle has 2 lines of symmetry.
4 a	36	The difference between the 4th and 5th term is 5 and between the 5th and 6th term is 6. The 5th term is 15 and the 6th term is 21. The sum of 15 and 21 is 36.
4 b	30	The LCM of a set of numbers is the smallest number that is a multiple of the numbers in that set. The 4th and 5th terms are 10 and 15, and the LCM is 30.
4 c	VI	The Roman numerals and their standard values up to 50 are I = 1, V = 5, X = 10, L = 50. The 3rd term is 6 which can be written as VI (5 + 1) in Roman numerals.
4 d	Triangular	There are no consecutive numbers, 1 is the only square and cube number. All numbers are triangular numbers; numbers that can be arranged as triangles using, for example, dots.
4 e	1	The only prime number of the first 4 terms is 3 so there is only 1 prime number.
5 a	35 minutes	The trains run every 40 minutes so at Grenham Central, trains are expected at 11:40, 12:20, 13:00 etc. If he arrives at 12:25, he has to wait 35 minutes for the train at 13:00.
5 b	2:00pm	It takes 20 minutes to travel between any 2 stations. If Jack leaves Grenham Central at 1:00pm, it take 3 x 20 minutes to reach Redmond so he reaches at 2:00pm.
5 c	2 hours 00 minutes	The original journey lasts 80 minutes. A 50% increase on this gives 120 minutes. Converting this into hours gives 2 hours.
5 d	£14.20	3 adults cost (3 x £3.20) and 2 children cost (2 x £2.30) which gives £9.60 + £4.60 = £14.20.

Short Test 8 Answers and Explanations

Question	Answer	Explanation
1 a	(-4,-2)	Rotating 180° about (0,0) from the top right quadrant gives a new shape in the bottom left quadrant. The new coordinates are (-4,-2).
1 b	(-4,2)	A reflection in the y axis is reflecting in the vertical lines. This gives new coordinates of (-4,2).
1 c	(4,6)	A square has 4 edges of equal length. Therefore, the only point the 4th corner can be is (4,6).
1 d	8 down, 4 right	A translation is moving a shape right, left, up or down a given number of squares. The translation from shape A to E is 8 units down and 4 units right.
2 a	38m	The perimeter is the total distance around the edge of any 2D shape. The perimeter of the shape is 38m (8 + 11 + 8 + 11 = 38).
2 b	6.5m²	Find 26 ÷ 4 which equals 6.5. The area of 1 flower bed is therefore 6.5m².
2 c	54m²	The inner rectangle has a width of 9m and a height of 6m. Therefore the area of the grass and flower beds is 54m² (9 x 6 = 54).
2 d	28m²	The total area of the grass and flower beds is 54m², and the area of the flower beds are 26m², so the area of the grass is 28m² (54 - 26 = 28).
2 e	14:13	The area of grass is 28m² and the area of the flower beds are 26m². The ratio is 28:26 which simplifies to 14:13.
3 a	19	The median is the middle number in a set of numbers when they are put in ascending or descending order. The middle value of the set 7, 14, 19, 23 and 32 is 19.
3 b	17.4	The mean is the number found by adding together all of the numbers and dividing by how many numbers there are in a set. Therefore the mean is (17 + 26 + 27 + 8 + 9) ÷ 5 = 17.4.
3 c	4	Russia won 24 gold medals. 1/6 of 24 is 4.
3 d	8	The HCF of a group of numbers is the largest number that is a factor of all numbers in that group. Therefore the HCF of 24 and 32 is 8.
3 e	56	The LCM of a set of numbers is the smallest number that is a multiple of the numbers in that set. The LCM of 7 and 8 is 56.
4 a	180°	The sum of the interior angles in a triangle is 180°.
4 b	34°	The sum of the angles in a triangle is 180°. Two of the angles of the triangle have been given; 56° and 90°. Therefore the size of angle $x°$ is 34° (180 - 90 - 56 = 34).
4 c	Isosceles	An isosceles triangle has 2 equal sides and 2 equal angles. It cannot be a right-angled triangle because the size of angle $y°$ is not 45°.
4 d	1	A shape has symmetry when it can be divided into 2 equal mirror images. An isosceles triangles has 1 line of symmetry.
4 e	50°	Angles on a straight line add to 180°. 2 of the angles on the line are given; 56° and 74°. Therefore the size of angle $y°$ is 50° (180 - 56 - 74 = 50).
5 a	9	Find 81 + 3³ = 81 + 9 = 108, and then divide by 12 which equals 9.
5 b	12	The positive square root of 144 is 12.
5 c	45	The input from number machine 1 is 9 and from number machine 2 is 5. (121 - 4² = 121 - 16 = 105, divided by 21 which equals 5). The product of 5 and 9 is 45 (5 x 9 = 45).
5 d	63	The output from number machine 3 is 144 and the output from number machine 1 is 81 so 144 - 81 = 63.
5 e	45	The input from number machine 1 is 9 and from number machine 2 is 5. The LCM of 5 and 9 is 45.

Short Test 9 Answers and Explanations

Question	Answer	Explanation
1 a	**260**	There are 360⁰ in a circle and there are 720 children (360 x 2 = 720). The size of the angle representing red i 130⁰ so the number of children who chose red is 260 (130 x 2 = 260).
1 b	**170**	The number of children who preferred red was 260 and the number of children who preferred green is 90. The difference between 260 and 90 is 170 (260 - 90 = 170).
1 c	**10:9**	The number of children who preferred blue was 100 and the number of children who preferred green was 90. The ratio is 100:90 which simplifies to 10:9.
1 d	**D**	$^1/_8$ of 360⁰ is 45⁰. The angle representing green is equal to 45⁰ so the answer is D.
1 e	**108**	Finding 15% of 720 gives 108 (720 x 0.15 = 108).
2 a	**A**	A shape has symmetry if it can be divided into 2 equal, mirror images. Shape A has 5 lines of symmetry and is the only shape that has more than 4 lines of symmetry.
2 b	**3**	Rotational symmetry is when you turn a shape around the centre to see how often it maps onto itself. An equilateral triangle has rotational symmetry of order 3.
2 c	**B and C**	A shape has symmetry when it can be divided into 2 equal, mirror images. Shapes B and C both have only 1 line of symmetry.
2 d	**108⁰**	All the interior angles in a regular pentagon are equal. The total sum of angles in a regular pentagon are 540⁰. The size of one interior angle is 108⁰ (540 ÷ 5 = 108)
2 e	**60⁰**	All the interior angles in an equilateral triangle sum to 180⁰. Therefore the size of one interior angle is 60⁰ (180 ÷ 3 = 60).
3 a	**-4.0⁰C**	Reading the value from the diagram gives - 4.0 ⁰C.
3 b	**3.6⁰C**	The original temperature is -4.0⁰C and it rises by 7.6⁰C to give 3.6⁰C (-4.0 + 7.6 = 3.6).
3 c	**-1⁰C**	The mean is the number found by adding together all of the numbers and dividing by how many numbers there are in a set. Adding all the numbers together gives -7⁰C and dividing by 7 gives -1⁰C (-7 ÷ 7 = -1).
3 d	**14⁰C**	The range of a set of numbers is the difference between the smallest and largest number. The difference between 8⁰C and -6⁰C is 14⁰C.
3 e	**1⁰C**	The median is the middle number of a set when put in order of size and the mode is the number in a set tha occurs most often. The median value is -1⁰C and the mode is 0⁰C so the difference is 1⁰C.
4 a	$^3/_8$	A cube number is the product of a number that is multiplied by itself twice e.g. 2 x 2 x 2 = 8. There are 3 cube numbers; 1, 8 and 27. Of a total of 8 cards, the probability of choosing a cube number is $^3/_8$
4 b	$^3/_8$	A triangular number is a number that can be arranged as a triangle using, for example, dots. There are 3 triangular numbers; 1, 3 and 6. As the total number of cards is 8, the probability of choosing a triangular number is $^3/_8$.
4 c	**900**	Find the value of the digit 9 wherever it appears in the number. In 6918, the value of the digit 9 is 900.
4 d	**1:3**	There are 2 even numbers and 6 odd numbers. The ratio of even to odd is 2:6 which simplifies to 1:3.
4 e	**3**	Prime numbers have only 2 factors: one and the number itself. There are 3 prime numbers in the set; 3, 7 and 11. Note that 1 is not a prime number.
5 a	**17:00**	London is 8 hours ahead of Los Angeles. If the time in Los Angeles is 9:00am, in London it will be 5:00pm which is 17:00 in 24 hour format.
5 b	**10:50pm**	Adding two hours to 8:50pm gives 10:50pm.
5 c	**22:50**	The 24-hour clock uses the hours 0:00 to 24:00 with 12:00 being midday. Converting 10:50pm into 24-hour format gives 22:50.
5 d	**5**	The difference in hours between 4:23am and 9:23am is 5 hours.
5 e	**£699.00**	For 2 adults and 1 child, the sum required is (250 x 2) + 199 = 699 so total price is £699.00.

Short Test 10 Answers and Explanations

Question	Answer	Explanation
1 a	5	Each term in the sequence increases by 5 (e.g. 16 - 11 = 5).
1 b	2	A triangular number is a number that can be arranged as a triangle using e.g. dots. There are 2 triangular numbers in sequence B; 3 and 6.
1 c	96	Each term in sequence B is the previous term doubled. Therefore the next term in the sequence will be 48 x 2 = 96.
1 d	45	The range of a set of numbers is the difference between the smallest and largest number. Of the first 4 terms, the largest number is 48 and the smallest number is 3 so the difference is 45 (48 - 3 = 45).
1 e	1.0	Each term in sequence C is a third of the preceding term. Therefore the next term is 3 ÷ 3 = 1.0.
2 a	200cm	The maximum capacity of the trough is 160,000cm³, and the cross-sectional area is 800cm² so the length of X is 200cm (160,000 ÷ 800 = 200).
2 b	32	The maximum capacity of the trough is 160,000cm³, and each pig requires 5,000cm³ so the trough is sufficient for 32 pigs per day (160,000 ÷ 5000 = 32).
2 c	4	The maximum capacity of the trough is 160,000cm³ and one horse requires 40,000cm³, the trough provides enough water for 4 days (160,000 ÷ 40,000 = 4).
2 d	800000cm³	The maximum capacity of the trough is 160,000cm³, and after 5 days, the total volume of water that can fill the troughs is 800,000cm³ (160,000 x 5 = 800,000).
2 e	£2693.75	If one trough costs £538.75, 5 troughs will cost £2693.75 (538.75 x 5 = 2693.75).
3 a	50	The total number of sweets bought in one day was 10, so for 5 days, the total number of sweets is 50 (10 x 5 = 50).
3 b	$^2/_5$	The number of lemon sweets bought in one day was 4 and the total number of sweets bought in one day was 10. The fraction of lemon sweets is $^4/_{10}$ which simplifies to $^2/_5$.
3 c	30%	The number of orange sweets bought in one day was 3 and the total number of sweets bought in one day was 10. The fraction of orange sweets is $^3/_{10}$ which is 30% as a percentage.
3 d	3:4	The number of strawberry sweets bought in one day was 3 and the number of lemon sweets bought in one day was 4. The ratio of strawberry to lemon is 3:4.
3 e	50%	The total number of sweets are now 6 and there are 3 strawberry sweets so the percentage of strawberry sweets is 50%.
4 a	9000g	To convert kilograms into grams, multiply by 1000. The value of the diagram is 9kg or 9000g.
4 b	600g	There are 15 spheres and the total mass is 9000g. Therefore the mass of one sphere is 600g (9000 ÷ 15 = 600).
4 c	4/15	There are 4 black spheres and the total number of spheres is 15, so the fraction of black spheres is $^4/_{15}$.
4 d	800g	The original mass was 9000g and the mass including the cube is 9800g so the difference in mass is 800g (9800 - 9000 = 800).
4 e	4:6:5	There are 4 black spheres, 6 grey spheres and 5 white spheres. The ratio of black to grey to white is 4:6:5.
5 a	5 feet	If there are roughly 30cm in one foot, there will be 5 feet in 150cm (150 ÷ 30 = 5).
5 b	65.0cm	$^{13}/_{30}$ of 150cm is 65.0cm (150 ÷ 30 x 13).
5 c	125.0cm	$^5/_6$ of 150cm is 125.0cm (150 ÷ 6 x 5).
5 d	180.0cm	Dividing 150 by 6 and then multiplying by 6 gives 180.0cm (150 ÷ 5 x 6).
5 e	132.5cm	Substituting 150 for j gives m = (0.75 x 150) + 20 = 132.5cm.

BLANK PAGE